A ROOKIE READER®

A BUZZ IS PART OF A BEE

By Carolyn Lunn

Illustrations by Tom Dunnington

Prepared under the direction of Robert Hillerich, Ph.D.

SCHOLASTIC INC.

New York   Toronto   London   Auckland   Sydney
Mexico City   New Delhi   Hong Kong   Buenos Aires

9   10   62   11 10 09

A leaf is part of a tree.

A buzz is part of a bee.

A wheel is part of a skate.

A latch is part of a gate.

A thorn is part of a rose.

A freckle is part of a nose.

An elbow is
part of an arm.

9

10

A barn is part of a farm.

A pea is part of a pod.

A hook is part of a rod.

Candles are part of a cake.

A handle is part of a rake.

A tail is part of a kite.

Dark is part of the night.

A lace is part of a shoe.

A keeper is part of a zoo.

A pit is part of a peach.

Sand is part of the beach.

Bubbles are part of a bath.
Stones are part of a path.

A caboose is part of a train.

Stripes are part of a cane.

A fish is part of the sea

and my shadow is part of ME!

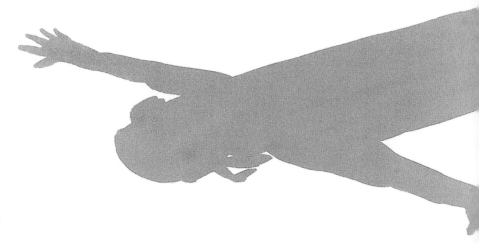

WORD LIST

			rose
a	cane	leaf	sand
an	dark	me	sea
and	elbow	my	shadow
are	farm	night	shoe
arm	fish	nose	skate
barn	freckle	of	stones
bath	gate	part	stripes
beach	handle	path	tail
bee	hook	pea	the
bubbles	is	peach	thorn
buzz	keeper	pit	train
caboose	kite	pod	tree
cake	lace	rake	wheel
candles	latch	rod	zoo

About the Author

Carolyn Lunn is an American, now living in England with her British husband and three-year-old son. As well as writing stories, she enjoys running, cooking, and gardening. Her other books include *A Whisper Is Quiet*, *Bobby's Zoo*, and *Purple Is Part of a Rainbow*.

About the Artist

Tom Dunnington divides his time between book illustration and wildlife painting. He has done many books for Childrens Press, as well as working on textbooks, and is a regular contributor to "Highlights for Children." Tom lives in Oak Park, Illinois.